# SEVEN SEAS ENTERTAINMENT PRESENTS

## The Ancient Magus' Bride
### VOLUME 15

story and art by **KORE YAMAZAKI**

TRANSLATION
**Adrienne Beck**

ADAPTATION
**Ysabet Reinhardt MacFarlane**

LETTERING AND RETOUCH
**Lys Blakeslee**
**Rachel Pierce**

INTERIOR LAYOUT
**Sandy Grayson**

COVER DESIGN
**Nicky Lim**

PROOFREADER
**Dawn Davis**

EDITOR
**Alexis Roberts**

PREPRESS TECHNICIAN
**Rhiannon Rasmussen-Silverstein**

MANAGING EDITOR
**Julie Dav**

ASSOCIATE PUB

FOLLOW US ONLINE: **www.sevenseasentertainment.com**

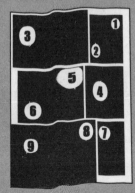

# READING DIRECTIONS

This book reads from *right to left*, Japanese style.
If this is your first time reading manga, you start
reading from the top right panel on each page and
take it from there. If you get lost, just follow the
numbered diagram here. It may seem backwards at
first, but you'll get the hang of it! Have fun!!

This otherworldly fairytale of romance and learning to accept the world continues in volume 16! Coming Soon!

The forbidden tome that was supposedly stolen is still hidden somewhere inside the College. Why keep it there? The College faculty is left scratching their heads over what the culprit is truly after. Meanwhile, life under lockdown helps bring Chise and the other pupils closer together...but that very closeness brings tension, and small misunderstandings lead ...ger suspicion. What ...hen someone finally ...ads that have ...ht...?

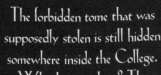

Even the drowning must reach out their hand to be saved.

# AFTERWORD

There sure was a lot of snow this year...

THANKS AS ALWAYS FOR PURCHASING *THE ANCIENT MAGUS' BRIDE* VOLUME 15!

THAT'S A VOLUME NUMBER I NEVER THOUGHT I'D REACH. YOU'VE ALL LET ME DRAW SO MUCH!

THIS WINTER WAS PARTICULARLY COLD AND SNOWY...

AND PARTICULARLY HARD ON MY HEALTH.

I'M PROBABLY JUST GETTING OLD, TOO.

Not being able to go outside due to the pandemic was also added stress.

Volume 15! When did we get that high?!

EVERYONE, PLEASE TAKE CARE OF YOURSELVES!

REMEMBER TO REST AND TAKE IT EASY, OKAY?

Hot water bottles.

Hot bath.

Hot food.

KOTATSU

Hot drinks.

OH! I'M MAKING STEADY PROGRESS ON MY NEW WORK, TOO. BE SURE TO CHECK IT OUT!

Lots of snow to shovel this year, too!

SO, I'LL SEE YOU IN THE AUTUMN!

I HOPE YOU'LL LOOK FORWARD TO WHAT HAPPENS IN THE NEXT VOLUME!

THE MAIN STORYLINE HAS BEEN STEADILY TRUNDLING ALONG SO FAR, BUT NOW...

SOME OF THE KIDS ARE FINALLY STARTING TO SPEAK UP ABOUT THEIR REAL THOUGHTS!

ALL.

Wow!

WITHDRAWN

I SEE. THEN SHALL WE...

CHAT AS WE STROLL?

!

IT SEEMS SHE'S FINALLY MADE A FRIEND AFTER ALL.

KINDA?

UM!

I'M CONCERNED...

WELL...

LET ME TELL YOU A STORY. ONE SEEMINGLY TOO MINOR TO HAVE CAUSED ANYTHING.

A STORY THAT UNFOLDED NOT TOO FAR IN THE PAST.

To be continued...

BUT THAT IS UNQUESTIONABLY THE CASE WITH HOUSE RICKENBACKER.

WADING INTO SUCH WATERS ON A WHIM MAY COST YOU **DEARLY,** AND--CHISE?

I'VE DONE THAT. I DOVE INTO SOMEONE ELSE'S PERSONAL LIFE...

AND I LIVED THROUGH THE **PAIN** THAT FOLLOWED.

EYES THAT SEEM UNTHINKING, YET ALSO SEEM TO SEE THROUGH EVERYTHING...

THEY'RE ALMOST THE EYES OF A BEAST.

SO, SHE **DOES** WEAR SUCH EXPRESSIONS.

YOU MUST BE VERY FOND OF PHILOMELA.

HUH?!

I THOUGHT HER FAMILY, THE SARGANTS...

WAS IN SERVICE TO YOURS-- TO HOUSE RICKENBACKER.

REALLY...?

HAVE YOU EVER BEEN BOUND BY SOMETHING?

CHISE.

MISS MAGE.

SO YOU IMAGINE I CAN WAVE A HAND AND SOLVE EVERYTHING?

HEE HEE.

I CAN'T SPEAK FOR OTHER HOUSES...

SOCIETY LOVES ITS TALK OF FREEDOM THESE DAYS, BUT OUTSIDE THE PUBLIC EYE, MUCH IS STILL FORBIDDEN.

PEOPLE LIKE ME ARE BOUND BY OUR HOUSES THE MOMENT WE'RE BORN.

"BOUND"...?

STORIES LIKE THEIRS ARE FAMILIAR HERE.

THE COLLEGE'S PUPILS SOMETIMES INCLUDE SUCH CHILDREN.

......

SPEAKING OF STORIES...

PHILOMELA WAS TOLD SHE HAS TO **WITHDRAW** FROM THE COLLEGE FOR FAMILY REASONS.

DO YOU **KNOW** THAT STORY?

I'VE HEARD, OF COURSE, BUT THERE'S LITTLE I CAN DO.

Urk!

AH, THERE'S YOUR QUESTION.

YOU HAVEN'T A KNACK FOR SUBTLETY.

YES. THEY'RE THE ONLY TWO LIVING MEMBERS OF THE ATWOOD FAMILY.

THE ATWOOD SIBLINGS, WHO KINDLY SPEND TIME WITH ME, ARE TWELVE AND ELEVEN.

EVEN AT THAT YOUNG AGE, THEY'RE WELL EDUCATED.

OUR FAMILY TOOK THEM IN, SO WE MADE CERTAIN OF THAT.

YOU TOOK THEM IN?

THEIR PARENTS WERE DOING IMPORTANT RESEARCH...

BUT, EVIDENTLY, SOMEONE DECIDED THEY WANTED THAT RESEARCH FOR THEMSELVES.

ALL BECAUSE THEY WERE BORN TO AN ALCHEMIST FAMILY.

THOSE TWO WERE THE ONLY SURVIVORS.

THE POOR THINGS.

HER SCENT IS SO HARD TO FIGURE OUT.

I...DON'T REALLY HAVE MUCH EXPERIENCE TALKING TO PEOPLE.

YOU'RE **FIDGETING** LIKE THERE'S SOMETHING YOU WANT TO ASK.

BUT I THINK YOU HAVE IT IN YOU. YOU CHAT NATURALLY WITH RIAN AND LUCY.

I'M AFRAID ONLY **PRACTICE** CAN HELP WITH THAT.

SHE'S LIKE SETH THAT WAY.

I'M SIXTEEN, BUT RIAN, ISAAC, AND PHILOMELA...

ARE ALL FIFTEEN.

THEY'RE **YOUNGER**?!

I'LL TAKE *THAT* AS A COMPLIMENT.

YOU SEEM SO GROWN UP, VERONICA. ARE WE REALLY THE SAME AGE?

WITHIN ONE GRADE, PUPILS CAN BE TWO OR THREE YEARS APART.

COULD YOU KINDLY ADD THE STAMP?

THE HALL WHERE THEY SAY THE BODY OF A MAN WHO LOST HIS HEAD IN AN EXPERIMENT WAS FOUND.

SURE.

THERE ARE SO MANY THINGS I WANT TO ASK HER...

BUT HOW DO I START...?

YOU KNOW, CHISE...

YOU'RE AWFULLY GENTLE. SHY, EVEN.

HUH?

FOLK LIKE US CAN'T GET BY IF WE DON'T **VENT** ONCE IN A WHILE...

YOU KNOW?

*THERE ARE STILL SOME THINGS WE NEED...*

*BEFORE WE CAN MOVE FORWARD FROM HERE.*

HERE'S THE FOURTH.

KLOK...

KLOK...

LOOKS LIKE THE NEXT ONE'S UP-STAIRS.

WE'RE BOUND, ALL OF US.

WE CAN'T MOVE OR ACT. IT'S SO STIFLING.

BOUND BY THE OUTSIDE WORLD. BOUND BY OUR-SELVES.

SAY, PHILOMELA.

THAT'S WHY...

YEAH...

HE NEVER DID LEARN TO READ BETWEEN THE LINES.

HE'S SO STRAIGHT-FORWARD.

I CAN'T MAKE MYSELF HATE ALL OF HIM. S'POSE THAT'S WHY I CAN STAY FRIENDS WITH HIM.

BUT FOR ALL THAT... HE'S SUCH A GOOD AND HONEST GUY IT TICKS ME OFF.

IT'S ENOUGH... TO MAKE YOU SICK.

THE THING ABOUT RIAN IS, HE BELIEVES HE'S NOT TALENTED.

HE THINKS IF HE CAN DO SOMETHING, **EVERYONE** CAN.

YOU KNOW WHAT I MEAN.

⋮

HE CAN'T WRAP HIS HEAD AROUND SOMEONE BEING UNABLE TO ACT. OR TRY.

WHEN SOME-BODY JUST **CAN'T**...

YOU'RE...

I THINK IT'D DO HIM **GOOD** TO HEAR IT FROM YOU, REALLY.

YOU DON'T NEED TO KEEP WHAT I SAID A SECRET FROM HIM.

Aha! Success.

RIGHT?

Y... YEAH.

I COULD NEVER BEST RIAN AT ANYTHING.

IT'S EMBAR-RASSING TO ADMIT, BUT I'M THE TYPE WHO LEARNS BY MESSING UP FIRST.

'SPECIAL-LY IN MY CASE.

WHENEVER I GOT DOWN, I COULDN'T FOCUS WHEN LEARNING THE FAMILY TRADE.

YOU MIGHT NOT THINK IT, BUT IT CAN BE A ROYAL PAIN BEING FRIENDS WITH...

SOMEONE THE SAME AGE AND GENDER AS YOU. PEOPLE COMPARE YOU.

YOU AND I, WE'VE BOTH BEEN THE TARGETS OF SOME VICIOUS TONGUES.

. . . . . . .

AND WHEN YOU WORK WITH FIRE AND MOLTEN METAL, TINY SLIPUPS LEAD TO BIG TROUBLE.

I CONSIDER YOU A **FRIEND**, SO I CAN'T LOOK THE OTHER WAY.

WHA...?

ABOUT RÍAN, BUT ABOUT A HEAP OF OTHER STUFF, TOO, I'D WAGER.

YOU'VE GOT A WHOPPING **INFERI-ORITY COMPLEX**, RIGHT?

Y-YOU'RE A BLACK-SMITH FAMILY.

HOUSE SCRIMGEOUR HAS RELIED ON YOUR FAMILY'S CRAFT FOR GENERATIONS.

B-BUT YOU'RE RÍAN'S FRIEND-- AND A **FOWLER**.

WE NEVER BUMPED INTO EACH OTHER BEFORE COMING HERE.

SINCE RÍAN WAS ALWAYS THE ONE TO COME VISIT ME...

YOU AREN'T LIKE THE SARGANTS. W-WE'RE USED AS **SHADOWS**.

UM...

I'LL LET THE OTHERS KNOW WHEN I FINISH.

VERONICA PROBABLY DRAGGED YOU ALONG, RIGHT?

I'VE NOTICED YOU DEFENDING ME A LOT LATELY.

WHY?

HOW DOES IT BENEFIT YOU?

I HAVEN'T DONE ANYTHING TO EARN THAT...

FROM YOU.

TH-THEN, UM...

URK!

YOU'D BE IN TROUBLE IF YOU GOT STARTLED AND YOUR **SNAKES** POPPED OUT, RIGHT?

THEY SAID IT WAS OKAY, BUT--

WHY'D YOU **SWAP PARTNERS** TO BE WITH ME?

BESIDES...

LATELY, TRYING TO TALK TO ANYONE BUT YOU AND THE OTHERS FEELS LIKE TOO MUCH BOTHER.

OH...

YEAH.

CAN'T SAY I EVER IMAGINED GOING FOR A NIGHTTIME HORROR TOUR THROUGH THE COURTYARDS.

ARE YOU SCARED?

I'M USED TO THE DARKNESS OF NIGHT FROM HOME. THE DARKNESS INSIDE A BUILDING JUST...ISN'T SCARY.

AH. YEAH.

SHE WAS SO TIMID ABOUT IT THAT I WOULD'VE FELT LIKE I WAS BULLYING HER IF I SAID NO!

FROM THE SOUNDS OF IT, I COULD'VE INVITED HER AND SHE STILL MIGHT'VE COME.

CHISE INVITED ME.

SHE DID?

I'M SURPRISED YOU'RE HERE, THOUGH. WOULDN'T'VE EXPECTED IT TO BE YOUR THING.

SO...

THIS IS THE FIRST?

WELL, I DOUBT ANYTHING'S **REALLY** LINGERING.

THE TREE WHERE A PUPIL SUPPOSEDLY HANGED THEMSELF DECADES AGO.

LET ME STAMP THIS QUICK.

IS THAT STORY EVEN TRUE? IT SOUNDS MADE UP TO ME.

ALL RIGHT, WE'LL ADD ANOTHER LOT AND... NOW, ON THREE...

ONE.

TWO.

THREE!

HMM... HOW ABOUT WE--

JASMINE ...?

EXCUSE ME!

WERE YOU REALLY ALL PLANNING TO GO HAVE FUN WITHOUT ME? THAT'S TERRIBLE!

JUST DON'T OVERDO IT, JASMINE.

SHOULDN'T YOU BE RESTING?

I'M FEELING A LITTLE BETTER.

I WON'T, I WON'T.

SMILE

YOU'D BEST NOT GIVE ME YOUR COLD.

THEN...

AT EACH LOCATION, THERE'S A **STAMP** TO MARK YOUR SHEET.

IF YOU WANT TO TRADE PARTNERS, SEE IF YOU CAN WORK IT OUT.

WE'LL DRAW LOTS TO ASSIGN **PAIRS.**

HERE'S HOW IT'LL WORK!

ONCE YOU HAVE ALL SEVEN STAMPS, HEAD FOR THE END POINT. THAT'S IT!

YOUR ROUTE'S ON THE PAPER YOU WERE GIVEN.

ONCE WE'RE ALL PAIRED, EACH PAIR WILL FOLLOW A SET ROUTE THROUGH THE LOCATIONS.

"HAVEN'T TOLD THE PROFESSORS," HUH...?

ALL RIGHT? ALL RIGHT.

I PUT A LOT OF WORK INTO MAKING THOSE STAMPS, SO BE SURE TO USE THEM!

A PAIR WILL SET OUT EVERY FIVE MINUTES.

WITH THE CATS WATCHING, EVERYTHING SHOULD BE OKAY.

GLANCE

YOU'LL VISIT EACH OF THE **SEVEN** SPOTS, ONE BY ONE.

AT THE END OF OUR TOUR, WE'LL SCREEN A **HORROR MOVIE** IN THE OBSERVATORY.

**6.**

A **ROOM** WHERE YOU CAN HEAR THE VOICE OF SOMEONE WHO SUMMONED **SOMETHING** AND VANISHED.

**5.**

A **CURSED MIRROR** THAT, IF YOU ANSWER YOUR REFLECTION'S CALL, WILL ENSNARE YOU.

**7.**

THE **OBSERVATORY POOL** THAT DROVE ONE PROFESSOR TO MADNESS AND SUICIDE.

ALL RIGHT! HERE'S THE GIST OF TONIGHT'S EVENT.

THERE'RE SEVERAL LOCATIONS IN THE COLLEGE WITH **SCARY** HISTORIES.

**2.**

A **COURTYARD** WHERE, TWENTY YEARS AGO, A MISSING PUPIL'S DESICCATED REMAINS WERE FOUND.

**1.**

A **TREE** WHERE A PUPIL HANGED THEMSELF THIRTY-TWO YEARS AGO. THEIR BODY WAS COVERED IN STRANGE SCRATCHES.

**4.**

A **HALL** WHERE THE BODY OF A MAN WHO LOST HIS HEAD IN AN EXPERIMENT WAS FOUND.

**3.**

A **STAIRWELL WINDOW** THAT'S BELIEVED TO BE CURSED. IF YOU LOOK INTO IT, YOU'LL SEE HOW YOU DIE.

THANK YOU FOR PARTICIPATING IN TONIGHT'S TEST OF COURAGE!

IS OUR WHOLE CLASS HERE?

I THINK THE YOUNG TWINS ARE SOUND ASLEEP.

YOU THINK I'D MISS SOMETHING LIKE THIS?

NO ONE MADE YOU COME.

COULDN'T WE DO THIS NEXT WEEK? MY REPORT'S NOT FINISHED.

NOW, LET'S HAVE A WARM, QUIET GOLF-CLAP FOR CHISE, WHO FIRST SHARED THE IDEA!

CLAP
CLAP
CLAP
CLAP
CLAP

WE MUST BE SNEAKY TONIGHT!

I HAVEN'T TOLD THE PROFESSORS ABOUT THIS. KEEP YOUR VOICES LOW!

WITHOUT A BREAK FROM STUDYING, MY BRAIN'LL GO TO MUSH.

I JUST GOT AN INTERESTING IDEA. YOU WANT IN?

SILENCE...

ALL RIGHT.

WELCOME, BRAVE ADVENTURERS.

KIDS DO THINGS LIKE SNEAK INTO SCHOOL AT NIGHT AND LOOK AROUND...

OR GO VISIT PLACES WHERE SCARY THINGS'RE SUPPOSED TO HAVE HAPPENED.

YEAH...

IT WAS NEVER REALLY MY THING, BUT...

HUNH.

YOU'VE DONE THOSE THINGS?

SHAAA

HMM.

School activities and stuff.

A FEW TIMES, YEAH.

IT NEVER TURNED OUT WELL FOR ME, SO I ALWAYS LEFT PARTWAY THROUGH.

RIGHT NOW, MY SISTER, WHO I SPEND ALL MY TIME WITH, IS ILL.

SO I'M TOTALLY AT LOOSE ENDS.

THAT'S WHEN ALL OUR STORIES SAY THE DEAD COME HOME.

YEAH, BUT THEY'RE MORE OF A **SUMMER** THING.

OOH...! YOU HAD GHOSTS IN JAPAN, TOO, RIGHT?

THIS **DOES** SEEM DIFFERENT FROM WHEN SHE'S WITH STELLA.

I FEEL NO ODD EMOTIONS WELLING UP, THOUGH, PERHAPS I FEEL...

SUMMER'S WHEN KIDS HAVE TESTS OF COURAGE, AND I THINK...

THAT'S WHEN HAUNTED HOUSES ARE OPEN FOR THE SEASON.

"TESTS OF COURAGE"?

A BIT LONELY.

GHOSTS, I'D GUESS?

THERE'VE BEEN A LOT LATELY.

!

WINTER IS THE SEASON FOR GHOSTS AND THE LIKE, THOUGH.

REALLY?

SOMETIMES I CAN, SOMETIMES I CAN'T.

IT FEELS LIKE THERE'VE BEEN MORE THAN USUAL SINCE NOVEMBER.

CAN YOU SEE THEM, TOO?

OH, OF COURSE. THIS IS THAT TYPE OF SCHOOL.

WHERE ARE YOU FROM, CHISE?

JAPAN.

AH. ELIAS TOLD ME ABOUT THAT BEFORE.

THAT'S THE SEASON WHEN THE DEAD COME BACK HOME TO VISIT.

YEAH. AT LEAST IN THIS COUNTRY, WINTER'S ALWAYS BEEN THE BEST TIME FOR GHOST STORIES.

IT'S ALWAYS BEST TO START BY LEARNING FROM ONE'S ELDERS.

FOR MAGES, AND I SUPPOSE FOR ALCHEMISTS...

NO PROBLEM.

THANKS FOR LETTING ME BORROW YOUR MASTER SOMETIMES.

I DID THINK YOU TWO MIGHT BE MASTER AND APPRENTICE.

UM...

DOES HAVING EXACTLY THE RIGHT INSTRUCTOR FOR THESE THINGS MATTER THAT MUCH?

THOUGH, SOME ARE BETTER TEACHERS THAN OTHERS.

PLENTY OF ALCHEMISTS SURVIVE ON PURE INSTINCT.

BEING SELF-TAUGHT INEVITABLY LEADS TO TROUBLE.

WHEN PROBLEMS ARISE, YOU WON'T KNOW IF IT'S SAFE TO PUSH FORWARD.

ELDERS WILL HAVE A BETTER IDEA. SURVIVING FOR SO LONG MEANS THEY HAVE SOME SKILL AT AVOIDING DANGER.

SO! WHAT'VE YOU BEEN SEEING LATELY?

OH, UM...

AH. MAKES SENSE.

IF YOU WISH TO APPLY YOURSELF SERIOUSLY TO MAGIC, I SUGGEST YOU FIND A DIFFERENT TEACHER.

A MAGE WHO KNOWS ALCHEMY AND AN ALCHEMIST WHO KNOWS MAGIC ARE **VERY** DIFFERENT THINGS.

OH.

I GUESS THAT MAKES SENSE.

ONLY A FRACTION OF WHAT I'VE TAUGHT YOU SO FAR.

WHAT'VE YOU BEEN TEACHING THEM?

HE'S STILL GIVING MAGIC LESSONS?

RUFL RUFL

YOU ARE MY ONLY **TRUE** APPRENTICE. I HAVEN'T THE TIME TO TAKE ON COLLEGE PUPILS.

I'LL GIVE IT SOME THOUGHT.

EEP!

YES.

PROFESSOR, OUR NEXT MAGIC LESSON'S EARLY NEXT WEEK, RIGHT?

GREAT! I HAVE A QUES- TION.

N-NO, IT'S FINE.

HELLO, PROFESSOR AINSWORTH.

AM I INTER- RUPTING?

OKAY. JASMINE ISN'T FEELING WELL. I DOUBT SHE'LL BE ABLE TO ATTEND.

I THINK I'LL STAY WITH HER.

PROBABLY JUST AN EARLY WINTER COLD. NOTHING TO WORRY ABOUT.

DID SOME- THING HAPPEN TO HER?

AH. YOU'LL BE ABSENT.

VIOLET ST. GEORGE.

THAT'S UNSURPRISING IN WINTER, EVEN HERE WITHIN THE COLLEGE.

JUST BECAUSE IT'S WINTER?

I DON'T KNOW WHY, BUT IT FEELS LIKE...

MY SIGHT'S BEEN GLIMPSING MORE LATELY.

IS SOMETHING ABOUT?

CORRECT!

I'D NEVER CONFUSE YOU TWO.

VIOLET!

IT'D WORK IF WE **ROASTED** THEM IN THE OVEN FIRST.

TURNIPS AND PUMPKINS ARE BOTH UNSUITED TO GOING INTO SALADS, AFTER ALL.

WE...

THE TWO OF US...

HAVEN'T HAD A CHANCE TO CHAT IN A WHILE.

ELIAS...?

HM?

PLIP

AH. SHOWERS WERE PREDICTED.

PLIP

I LEFT A SMALL SHRED OF ITS CONSCIOUSNESS...

SO THAT IT WOULDN'T LOSE ALL SENSE OF SELF-PRESERVATION. YET...

BEASTS HEAL SO QUICKLY.

NO MATTER HOW YOU TINKER WITH THEIR BODIES, THEY'LL STILL RECOVER... EVENTU-ALLY.

ALL RIGHT.

I'LL RETURN THEM TO YOU.

IT'S JUST ABOUT TIME, ANYWAY.

Chapter 75: Needs must when the Devil drives. I

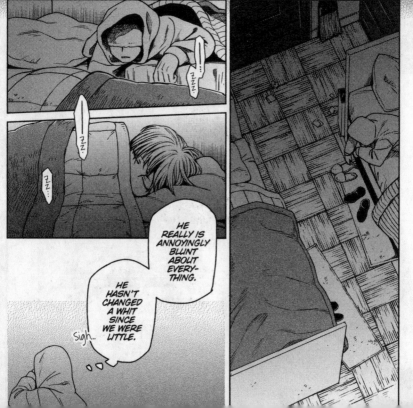

It's his **personality**, that's what. He's too **soft**. If he had the grit to try and claw his way back--

So he gets hurt too often. It's starting to look like his little sister's better suited.

He's falling behind for his age. He hasn't the **focus**, either.

Chapter 75: Needs must when the Devil drives. I

If he's not suited to this, we can send him **elsewhere**. That'd be best for him, too.

Well, it's too soon to completely write him off, I'd say.

I DON'T HAVE ANY RIGHT...

TO WANT ANYTHING.

WE WERE BORN IN COMPLETELY DIFFERENT SITUATIONS AND DIFFERENT SOCIAL POSITIONS.

OUR PERSONALITIES ARE TOTALLY DIFFERENT, SO OUR PROBLEMS MUST BE, TOO.

EVEN THOUGH...

WE WANT TO SAY WE DO.

WHAT CAN I POSSIBLY SAY TO HER?

WHENEVER I LOOK AT HER, I HAVE THIS SENSE OF FAMILIARITY AND CLOSENESS.

LOTS OF PEOPLE TOLD ME I'M FREE.

HOW DO I HELP HER LIKE THEY HELPED ME?

PHILO-
MELA...

IS THAT
WHAT
YOUR
GRAND-
MOTHER
TELLS YOU?

WHAT
DO *YOU*
WANT
TO DO?

BACK
THEN
OR
NOW?

I
DON'T...

*I KNOW THOSE EYES.*

HE'S... ALWAYS SO HONEST.

WE PLAYED GAMES.

COMPETED A LOT... AS KIDS.

*THOSE ARE EYES THAT CAN'T CRY.*

R....

RIAN AND I...

HE'D GET UPSET WHEN HE LOST, BUT HE...ALWAYS COMPLIMENTED ME FOR WINNING.

STORM

BETTER THAN BEING A STUCK-UP JERK!

YOU COULD TRY KEEPING YOUR NOSE OUT OF PEOPLE'S BUSINESS!!

WHACK

CLOMP

CLOMP

CLOMP...

SO I DON'T REALLY KNOW, BUT...IS IT NORMAL TO SAY THINGS LIKE THAT TO FRIENDS?

UM...

I'VE NEVER REALLY HAD FRIENDS BEFORE.

THIS IS JUST MY OPINION, THEN...

BUT I DON'T THINK IT'S VERY NICE TO TALK TO FRIENDS LIKE THAT. OR TO LADIES.

At least, not my idea of friends...

RIAN!

HOW COME SHE'S ALWAYS SO DOWN ON HERSELF?!

SHE'S WAY SMARTER THAN ME! AND BETTER AT ALCHEMY!

WHY DIDN'T SHE EVEN *TRY* TO BEAT ME?!

THAT'S...

PROBABLY WHAT SHE HAS TO DO TO SURVIVE.

SORRY, I'LL BE RIGHT BACK!

CHISE!

HON-ESTLY!

YEAH...

THEY'RE RELATED, AREN'T THEY?

WHAT'S UP WITH THOSE TWO?

JASMINE...?

EVERY-ONE'S GOT THEIR OWN PROBLEMS.

THINGS AREN'T...

LIKE THEY WERE.

DON'T GET YOUR HOPES UP...

AND BLAME ME WHEN YOU'RE LET DOWN.

RIAN...!

PHILO- MELA, ARE YOU ALL RIGHT?

NEED A MOMENT.

I...

S- SOR- RY.

YOU HELD BACK!

WHY?!

RIAN!

THERE'S NO WAY I COULD EVER FINISH ONE BEFORE YOU!

I'M TERRIBLE AT THIS GAME!

HEY! COOL YOUR TEMPER, YOU NUMPTY!

WHAT'S THIS ...?

My capacity for analyzing observations is fairly limited.

I envy that.

Is that so?
......

I COMPREHEND FEWER THAN **HALF** OF THE THINGS I OBSERVE.

DON'T BE.

BUT FOR SOME REASON, I FIND MYSELF CONTINUING TO RESPOND.

I HAVEN'T ANY NEED TO SPEAK WITH IT. I SHOULD SIMPLY IGNORE IT...

My apologies. I'm not skilled at maintaining conversation.

......

NO.

BUT FOR A CREATURE MADE BY HUMANS TO ALSO THINK THAT...

OTHER FAE HAVE OFTEN SAID I WEAR A SHELL OF FLESH.

PECULIAR?

Really? How peculiar.

?

IF ANYTHING, I'D SAY IT'S MORE THAT SHE LOOKS AFTER ME.

WE LOOK AFTER EACH OTHER, IN A WAY.

Are you here to look after her?

Oh, I beg your pardon.

I CAME TO OBSERVE.

What're they discussing?

Beings like me are created for a purpose, in order to be **useful** to our masters.

Yet you are **independent**.

I'M NOT AN ARTIFICIAL SPIRIT.

are you
and I
the
same?

"THE
SAME"?

WHAT
MAKES
YOU
THINK
SO?

One of the
new pupils
calls you
by name,
as well.

Is she
the one
you look
after?

I'm tempo-
rarily in a
fluid body
to perform
menial
tasks.

I thought
perhaps you
were wear-
ing **flesh**
for similar
reasons.

There's
Elias.

Hello.

GOOD DAY.

AH.

This is a rude question, I'm afraid, but may I ask...

We've met before, haven't we?

I HADN'T EXPECTED IT TO GREET ME.

THIS IS THAT FAMILIAR FROM EARLIER.

I PRESUME IT'S WATCHING OVER ITS MASTER.

BEGIN!

OH, HOW LOVELY!

YOU'VE ALWAYS HAD A **KNACK** FOR THIS SORT OF THING, RIGHT?

IF YOU REALLY DON'T WANT TO--

UM...

I- I...!

I'D **LOVE** TO WATCH YOU SOLVE ONE.

OKAY! SAME RULES AS BEFORE: WHOEVER UNLOCKS IT FIRST WINS.

SHOULD BE INTERESTING HAVING THESE TWO FACE OFF!

........

IF YOU WISH.

OH, I SEE!

PHILO-MELA.

FLINCH

IT'S BEEN AGES SINCE WE COMPETED WITH THESE.

THERE!

DONE!

KLUNK

YOU'RE THE LAST, ZOE.

AND RIAN.

BEA-TRICE...

THEN JAS-MINE...

MARTIN WAS.

WHO WAS FIRST?!

IT SEEMS THE GAME REALLY ISN'T FOR YOU.

YOU WERE FIRST, CHISE, BUT--

IT GOT YOU IN SOME TROUBLE THIS TIME, THOUGH, SETTING OFF THAT TRAP.

KA-POP

MAGIC IS AMAZING.

I HONESTLY DIDN'T THINK IT'D JUST...POP OPEN.

I...

I WONDER WHAT SORT OF MUSIC SHE WOULD LIKE.

CHISE'S NEVER BEEN ESPECIALLY FUSSY ABOUT ANYTHING.

SHE'LL EAT WHATEVER SHE'S SERVED WITHOUT COMPLAINT.

I RARELY HEAR HER MENTION PREFERENCES.

MAYBE I OUGHT TO ASK HER...

AH. THERE SHE IS.

IS HE BASHFUL, PERHAPS? OR SIMPLY QUITE INTROVERTED?

HE HAS THE AIR OF SOMEONE FAR OLDER, YET HE'S INCREDIBLY NAÏVE ABOUT THE WORLD.

BIP

ALL RIGHT.

THANK YOU.

I WONDER WHAT CD HE MIGHT LIKE...

WHAT A FASCINATING FELLOW.

PAP

MUSIC, HM?

I VAGUELY RECALL ANGELICA PUTTING ON RECORDS A WHILE BACK.

CHISE DOESN'T SEEM TO LISTEN TO MUCH.

OKAY.

I'LL GO IN, THEN.

THE ADDITIONAL **SECURITY** HAS TO DO WITH EVERYTHING THAT'S HAPPENED LATELY. TRY TO KEEP IT FROM THE CHILDREN, OKAY?

YES, I NOTICED SEVERAL GOLEMS ON PATROL.

DO YOU LIKE **MUSIC?**

. . . . . .

YOU DISLIKE IT?

AH, NO.

I'VE SIMPLY NEVER GIVEN IT MUCH THOUGHT, OR LISTENED TO MUCH.

AS A THANK-YOU, THEN, LET ME SEE IF I CAN FIND SOMETHING YOU MIGHT ENJOY.

MUSIC?

IF YOU NEED ANYTHING, YOU MAY CALL ON ME.

THANK YOU FOR WALKING ME OVER.

WELL, THESE ARE MY ROOMS.

HAS ANYONE EVER MENTIONED THAT YOU CAN BE OVERPROTECTIVE?

THANK YOU!

I assume that young lady is wearing one, too.

NOT TO WORRY, THOUGH. IF MY VITALS SO MUCH AS FLICKER, THIS'LL TELL ALEXANDRA AT ONCE.

I'LL BE CHECKING IN WITH HER OFTEN, UNTIL THINGS HAVE STABILIZED. BUT FOR NOW, I SHOULD BE FINE.

HA HA HA! TRUE, THAT!

BUT HUMANS ARE SO FRAIL.

UM...

OKAY.

YEAH. I WOULD, TOO.

OOH! AND I'D LOVE TO SEE MORE MAGIC!

IF YOU WANT TO, I DOUBT ANYONE WILL SAY NO.

MIGHT AS WELL.

I WILL.

SO! WHO WANTS TO MAKE THE FIRST LOCKS?

AND THE TEACHERS WON'T GET MAD IF THEY CATCH US!

MORE FUN, THOUGH, ISN'T IT?

ISN'T THIS STILL KINDA LIKE SCHOOL-WORK?

FOR ROUND ONE, WE'LL HAVE ONLY THREE LAYERS.

OKAY! ROY AND SOFIA, AND I THINK I WILL, TOO.

SOME KIND OF PUZZLE?

FIRST, A FEW PEOPLE LAYER **LOCK** SPELLS ON THE PUZZLE-- REAL SIMPLE ONES, LIKE FROM PRIMARY.

THEN OTHER PEOPLE RACE TO **UNDO** THE SPELLS AND TAKE IT APART.

HAVE YOU TWO NEVER PLAYED?

THESE ARE... HMM...AN ALCHEMY PRACTICE GAME.

IT ALL GETS PRETTY **COMPLEX**-- LIKE SEEING HOW MANY MATH PROBLEMS CAN EQUAL TEN.

AND SINCE THE ACTUAL LOCKS ARE SIMPLE, THEY REALLY SHOW OFF THE CASTER'S PERSONALITY.

YOU WANT TO LAYER THE LOCKS TIGHTLY, LIKE MAKING A PATCHWORK.

IT'S GOOD PRACTICE FOR ANALYSIS *AND* ENERGY CONTROL.

DON'T YOU HAVE A SPELL TO OPEN LOCKS?

I DO, BUT--

WHY NOT TRY IT JUST ONCE?

Alchemy huh?

I'M NOT SURE I COULD DO IT.

WOW.

Sounds interesting.

PRETTY MUCH!

SOUNDS TO ME LIKE YOU'RE ALL DESPERATE TO PUT YOUR MINDS TO ANYTHING BUT STUDYING RIGHT NOW.

A DECK OF CARDS OR SOMETHING?

NAH-- CARDS ARE FUN, BUT THERE'RE TOO MANY OF US.

I FIGURED WE WERE ALL HITTING THAT POINT, SO I BROUGHT A LITTLE SOMETHING ALONG.

RUSTLE !!

HERE!

I CAN GIVE IT A ONCE-OVER.

GREAT, THANKS.

WILL YOU CHECK MINE, TOO, ISAAC?

Hey!

GUH! NO HISTORY. I DON'T EVEN WANT TO **THINK** ABOUT HISTORY NOW!

ME, NEI- THER.

SO THIS IS WHAT A GROUP STUDY SESSION IS LIKE?

WITH THE LOCKDOWN, WE CAN'T GET ANY CHANGE OF SCENERY.

WE COULD GO SHOPPING OR GET LUNCH OR VISIT THE LIBRARY OR THE ZOO.

AT LEAST WHEN WE GOT SICK OF IT BEFORE, WE COULD DO SOMETHING ELSE.

IT'S TRUE, THOUGH. STUDYING'S EVEN MORE DULL THAN USUAL.

CABIN FEVER'S RUNNING RAMPANT, HUH?

I BET THE NEW ISSUE OF THAT COMIC I'M READING IS OUT BY NOW.

I COULD USE NEW CLOTHES.

I REALLY WANT TO GO EXPLORE NIFTY NEW SHOPS.

THERE'S PLENTY TO DO. LIKE STUDY.

THEN I'M JUST BORED, OKAY?!

THERE'S NOTHING TO DO!

CAN SOMEONE CHECK MY HISTORY OF ALCHEMY, THEN?

OOH! AND MINE!

MINE, TOO!

EXAMS ARE NEXT WEEK. DEAL WITH IT.

FLAIL

FLAIL

I'M SO SICK OF STUDYING FOR EXAMS...!

BUT WE CAN'T GO ANY- WHERE, EITHER!

LAZARUS, CAN YOU LOOK AT MY NUTRITION CALCULA- TIONS AND SEWING?

AWW...

YOUR WORK...

I THINK YOU SHOULD ASK HER THAT, NOT ME.

SPEAKING OF THAT...

HOW DID YOU AND CHISE MEET IN THE FIRST PLACE?

IT'D HELP YOU TWO UNDERSTAND EACH OTHER MORE.

BRZZ BRZZ

HM?

COME TO THINK OF IT...

ALL I KNOW OF CHISE'S LIFE IS RECENT. I KNOW SO LITTLE OF HER LIFE BEFORE WE MET.

DO YOU USE HUMAN TOILETS?

WHY ON EARTH ARE YOU ASKING?

I don't excrete at all, so no.

I HEARD YOU WERE UP AND ABOUT.

AH, AINSWOR-- ELIAS, RATHER.

CLOP

WHY ARE YOU LOOKING AT ME?

STARE

WELL, I'D BEST BE OFF.

I CAN'T EXACTLY DO ANY WORK WHILE I'M HERE.

IF I'LL BE HERE A WHILE, I'LL USE THE TIME TO ASK A FEW QUESTIONS.

BESIDES, I ORIGINALLY CAME BECAUSE MY SISTER COLLAPSED.

WITH THE COLLEGE IN LOCKDOWN, I CAN'T ACTUALLY GO HOME.

YOU'RE LEAVING?

Ah.

Chapter 74: Nothing ventured, nothing gained. IV

SO THE TERRIFYING TOME IS YET **WITHIN** OUR WALLS.

I SEE.

Inside the College.

YES?

The witches have completed their errand.

Vice-Chancellor.

PLEP

CRINKLE

WHY, THANK YOU, GATEKEEPER.

It's an honor!

HM.

YOU'RE AWFULLY PROTECTIVE OF HER. WHAT'RE YOU THINKING?

. . . . .

WHAT DO YOU THINK I'M THINKING?

?

WHAT ARE THEY DOING...?

I HATE WHEN PEOPLE DODGE MY QUESTIONS!

Aph!

Owph, owph, owph! Quiph pinching!! Yeowph!!

Ye-owch!!

PINCH
PINCH
PINCH
SKWEEEEZ

WE HAVEN'T TALKED SINCE THE OTHER DAY.

I WANTED TO ASK HOW SHE'S FEELING... HM?

CHISE. ZOE.

IT'S WEIRD. ALCYONE REMINDS ME OF ELIAS.

JUST... MORE CHILD-LIKE AND INNOCENT, SOMEHOW.

WAVE WAVE

NOW THEY'VE STARTED PATROLLING THE REGULAR FLOORS, TOO.

IT'S AS IF THEY'RE WATCHMEN.

ANYWAY. A LOT OF WHAT?

GOLEMS.

THERE WERE ALREADY A LOT ON THE GARDEN AND FIELD FLOORS.

I HAVEN'T MENTIONED ALL THAT, HUH?

THEN, THERE'S THE PROFESSOR WHO WAS ATTACKED, AND THAT SPELL BOOK THAT WAS STOLEN.

OH, YEAH. THERE WAS THE ATTACK ON LUCY...

THAT'S A GOOD POINT.

SETTING GUARDS SEEMS ONLY SENSIBLE.

SOMEONE ATTACKED SO HARD THAT THE WHOLE COLLEGE LOCKED DOWN.

THE WHOLE COLLEGE IS IN LOCKDOWN, BUT THEY JUST *HAD* TO MAKE SURE WE DON'T MISS EXAMS.

UGH... TESTS...

OOF. THAT MUST MAKE LESSONS AND EXAMS TRICKY.

I DIDN'T REALLY FOCUS ON IT UNTIL I MOVED TO ENGLAND.

DAD TAUGHT ME SOME, BUT WE USUALLY SPOKE THE VILLAGE LANGUAGE.

DON'T FORGET, IF YOU DON'T PASS YOUR SUMMER TEST, THEY'LL BRING YOU IN FOR **MAKE-UP EXAMS** OVER HOLIDAY.

LIKE CHRISTMAS HOLIDAY, EASTER HOLIDAY, SUMMER HOLIDAY...

MONTHLY CHECK-UP QUIZZES, A FULL EXAM BEFORE ALL LONG HOLIDAYS...

I'm so far behind...

Standard subjects!

IT'S SO HARD WHEN THEY USE ALL THESE **TECHNICAL TERMS** THAT DON'T COME UP IN DAILY CONVERSATION.

FOLLOWING THE LESSON MUST BE DIFFICULT, THEN.

BUT I STILL HAVE TO GET GOOD GRADES IN ALL THE GENERAL COURSES.

I'VE BEEN EXCUSED FROM THE ALCHEMY-RELATED EXAMS.

I DIDN'T FIGURE A MAGE WOULD NEED TO WORRY ABOUT THAT, CHISE.

THE STATION?

AYE.

Paddington Station

PEOPLE FROM THE COLLEGE, AT THAT.

AFTER ATTACKING ONLY TWO PEOPLE?

THEY MAY NOT EVEN BE IN LONDON ANYMORE.

TOOK A TAXI OR THE TUBE, MAYBE?

HERE'S WHERE IT VANISHES COMPLETELY.

BZZ BZ

BZZ BZ

OH...

A MESSENGER ALREADY?

SIMPLER AND LESS RISKY TO GO GOBBLING UP RANDOM PEOPLE WHO DON'T KNOW THEY'VE THE TALENT, I GUESS.

It's
almost
gone.

It's still
growing
fainter.

*Nnn...*

THEY'RE
WANDERING
IN CIRCLES
TO TRY TO
**CONFOUND**
US.

given the
massive
amount of
human traffic
flowing
through a city
this size.

Not like the
trail wasn't
hard enough
to follow
in the first
place...

I don't get
the feeling
they're
trying
to hide,
either.

It's
more
like...

THANKS!

If I spy anyone on the lookout, I'll let you know.

And should you wish to spend more good gold, please do think of me.

Hmm...

Well, that *is* disagreeable.

EEEUGH!

FEELS SO GROSS ...!!

SHWIP

Why *is* it that human creations are always so woefully incomplete?

BZZ

BZZ BZZ

Anyone carrying that book about will be noticed by even the greatest of fools.

There are more of them than there are stars in the sky.

MNN...!

A peculiar book?

Around here, everyone has **something** you might call peculiar.

TONK

If I may?

RAT

RAT

RAT

*Two* for a single coin. What say you?

These lovely **trick boxes** make splendid wards against imps! I'll even cut you a deal.

JA-KLANK

GU-
KRUK

I'll have you know I'm a witch, too.

And with a wolf-man companion, I see.

Well, well, well!

What brings you to my humble shop, good lady witch?

HAVE YOU NOTICED ANYONE WITH A PECULIAR BOOK LATELY?

It matters only that you're both human.

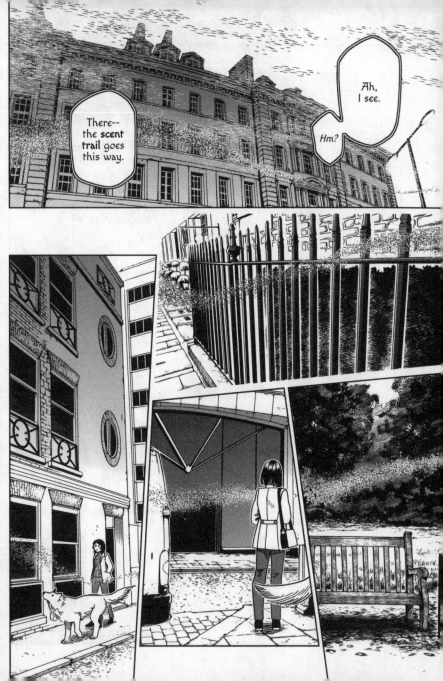

Witch or mage, for all our power...

if we try to handle everything that "fate" or whatever dumped in our laps, we'd have no freedom at all.

You're free to deny it, of course.

WELL, YES.

But you did draw the short straw, and I did get dragged along.

So?

That may be all it is.

Where and from whom did you get the grimoire?

A collector? An alchemist with dubious taste?

SO YOU ARE ASKING.

I SUPPOSE IT MUST HAVE BEEN... FIVE OR TEN YEARS AGO?

RIGHT AFTER PHYLLIS HAD TO WITHDRAW BECAUSE OF WHAT HAPPENED.

I LOOKED INTO EVERYTHING I COULD THINK OF, DESPERATE FOR A SOLUTION.

I EXPECTED MORE REACTION, BUT I SUPPOSE YOU ARE CENTURIES OLDER THAN ME.

NONE OF YOUR *LIP*, YOUNG 'UN!!

*EELIGH!!*

MPH...

Bleh!

IF YOU WEREN'T ONE OF US, I MIGHT'VE BITTEN YOU!

SHEESH...! YOU FIND ALL THE CREEPIEST JOBS.

DON'T THROW UP.

WHO DO YOU THINK YOU'RE TALKING TO?

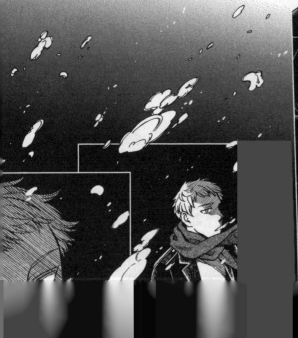

EXACTLY.

UNFORTUNATELY, DOING IT THE HARD WAY IS OUR ONLY OPTION.

IT'S A GRIMOIRE, YOU SAID.

WE'RE HUNTING THAT AND THE ONE WHO'S USING IT.

FOLLOWING LEADS AND ASKING AROUND.

UH, YOU'RE THE ONE WHO KNOWS THE **AURA**, MARIELLE. YOU SHOULD TAKE THE LEAD.

NOW GIVE ME MY **DIRECTIONS**, MISS NAVIGATOR! LET'S BE OFF!

YOU BET! I COULD LIVE FOR A **YEAR** OFF THIS MUCH IF I'M FRUGAL!

SO CAUTIOUS BEFORE, AND *NOW* LOOK AT YOU!

YOU'RE MORE INTO THIS THAN I EXPECTED.

I CAME TO YOU BECAUSE YOUR **NOSE** IS SHARPER THAN MINE.

PWUF

Don't ask me why, but we're **sealed** off.

What in the skies is hap-pening?

Are you the door-keeper?

I can't say for how long, as we've not been told.

If you want in, I fear you must wait.

Sealed?

"Resolu-tions team"...?

*Ugh!* How vexing.

I can say our resolutions team was sent out on errands.

Chapter 73: Nothing ventured, nothing gained. III

IT'S CLUMSIER AND SLOWER TO REACT THAN A HUMAN.

NOTHING, MA'AM.

IT SEEMS UNLIKELY IT CAN PROCESS, LET ALONE ENACT COMPLEX ORDERS.

AT BEST, I'D TAKE IT FOR A NURSE-MAID.

STP

IT'S YET UNCLEAR WHETHER OR NOT IT'S BEEN INFUSED WITH ANYTHING...

BUT, SO FAR, OBSERVATION SUGGESTS ITS CAPABILITIES ARE MINOR.

WE CAN ONLY WAIT AND SEE FOR NOW, I SUPPOSE.

AND THOSE WITH NO LEGAL GUARDIAN?

SHOULD THE ISSUE BE RESOLVED, THEY MAY REMAIN AS USUAL. SHOULD IT NOT BE...

I SUPPOSE WE COULD PUT THEM IN ONE LARGE ROOM AS IF THEY WERE PRIMARIES.

WE WILL REMAIN UNDER LOCKDOWN UNTIL **CHRISTMAS**, AS SCHEDULED.

ALL PUPILS WILL THEN BE TEMPORARILY RETURNED TO THEIR HOMES OR GUARDIANS.

HOW-EVER...

THAT **FAMILIAR** THAT'S ATTACHED TO PHILOMELA SARGANT.

HAS ANYTHING **ODD** BEEN NOTED?

AFTER THE INITIAL INCIDENTS, THERE'S YET TO BE ANOTHER ATTACK.

AND THE SARGANT FAMILY ISN'T PUSHING FOR THEIR CHILD'S WITHDRAWAL.

GREGORY.

Chapter 73: Nothing ventured, nothing gained. III.

OF COURSE. I'M PERFECT IN EVERY WAY.

YOU ALWAYS DID HAVE RIDICULOUSLY SHARP EYES AND EARS, HMM?

I WONDER WHAT'S MAKING THEM FEEL SO LONELY?

WE'RE DEFINITELY SPLITTING THE REWARD FIFTY-FIFTY, RIGHT?

WELL, START USING THOSE PERFECT SENSES TO TRACK THIS THING DOWN.

UGH... IT'D BE SO MUCH EASIER IF IT WERE A MISSING PERSON.

I CAN'T HELP WHAT I HEARD! IT'S NOT MY FAULT *YOU'RE* DEAF.

OKAY, AND?

Sheesh, you're powerfully empathetic.

What good witch isn't?

OH, HONESTLY, WHAT BROUGHT THAT ON?

PLIP. PLIP.

Urgh.

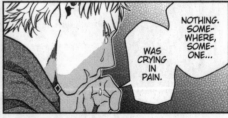

NOTHING. SOME- WHERE, SOME- ONE...

WAS CRYING IN PAIN.

I...
I have to go back.

CLUTCH

I can't take this...

Not any-more!

Go back...

Meet with them...

DEMAND THEM BACK...!

THIS LONELI-NESS...!

THIS SOLI-TUDE...

JOLT

HWOO...

GIVE
THEM
BACK!!!

HYU......

Play-
back
com-
plete.

Deleting
message.

If you
want to
see your
mother
and father
again...

you haven't
the time to
whine and
drag your
feet like a
spoilt child,
do you?

SQWZ

Miss
Philomela
...?

Are
you all
right?

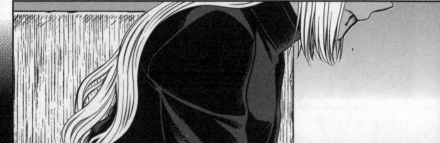

If you're simply going to fritter away this chance you've so generously been given...

then enough is enough.

Philomela.

SO SHE PRE-RECORDED THIS...? INTO ALCYONE...?

THE COLLEGE IS IN LOCKDOWN, SO NO MESSAGES SHOULD GET THROUGH.

GRAND-MOTHER'S...

VOICE...?

any such useless things will be disposed of. If you want to avoid that, carry out your duty.

COULDN'T RUN AWAY...!

should you be so foolish as to acquire friends...

SHE DID.

SO I...

An incompetent like you won't be welcomed home.

And any gains you make...

I DON'T KNOW...

BUT THIS... I JUST CAN'T...

BUT...

TAKE IT...!

Agh --!

ALCYONE ...?

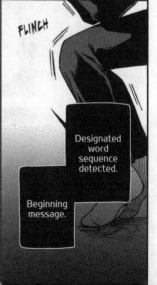

FLINCH

Designated word sequence detected.

Beginning message.

you told yourself you had to **obey.** You swallowed your complaints.

You gave up.

ALCYONE ...?

SHE'S ONE OF THE **IRREGULARITIES** I'M SUPPOSED TO MONITOR.

I CAN'T EVEN BEAR TO LOOK HER IN THE FACE...

BUT, SHE'S SO KIND TO ME.

！．．．

You're **different** now.

Why is that?

IT'S JUST...

SHE'S ...!

I... DON'T KNOW.

THERE'S NO WAY SHE COULD KILL A PERSON.

IF BREAKING A SIMPLE CONSTRUCT LEAVES HER IN THAT STATE...

THEY OUGHT TO HAVE A CLUE I CAN WORK WITH.

CLENCH

THE CHILD BACK THEN...

ABSOLUTELY EVERYONE HAS AN EGO.

BUT I ALSO DON'T TRUST PEOPLE WHO'RE ALWAYS FOCUSED ON OTHERS' NEEDS, NOT THEIR OWN.

THERE'S NO TELLING WHAT WILD NOTION THEY'LL GET NEXT.

SURE, PEOPLE WHO ONLY CARE ABOUT THEMSELVES ARE IRRITATING JERKS.

LUCY, YOU'RE REALLY NICE, TOO.

I CERTAINLY DON'T TRUST YOU, WITH YOUR ENDLESS HAREBRAINED SCHEMES.

HUH?! HOW COME?!

I WANTED TO ASK HER SOME THINGS.

BUT...

THAT REALLY DIDN'T FEEL LIKE THE RIGHT TIME.

SOME PEOPLE WANT TO CONSTRUCT THEIR BODIES IN VERY SPECIFIC WAYS.

AND THEY AREN'T THE ONLY ONES.

IT IS FOR THE FAMILIES PEOPLE TEND TO HAVE **GRUDGES** AGAINST.

OH.

EAT EXACT AMOUNTS OF THIS AND THAT. NEVER DO SOME STUFF AT ALL.

THAT REQUIRES BEING EXTREMELY RIGOROUS ABOUT A LOT OF THINGS.

I figured, since it didn't seem like she was drinking any.

AND PHILOMELA REALLY IS SUPER NICE.

NOTHING. IT'S JUST...I REALLY AM SELF-CENTERED.

MEANS WHAT?

THEN THAT MEANS...

........

WELL, *THAT* WAS A WASTE OF SPARKLING WATER.

· · · · · · ·

I HOPE SHE'LL BE OKAY.

HUH?

ANYTHING COULD'VE BEEN DONE TO IT.

YOU ABSOLUTELY MUSTN'T EAT, DRINK, OR USE IT.

BUT IF ANYONE ELSE GIVES YOU SOMETHING...

I GOT IT FROM THE CAFETERIA, SINCE IT'S CONSTANTLY MONITORED.

IS THAT KIND OF RISK **NORMAL** FOR ALCHEMISTS?

I GUESS HER FAMILY'S ONE OF THEM.

SOME FAMILIES BRING THEIR CHILDREN UP TO THINK THAT WAY.

OH.

SUIT YOUR-SELF, THEN.

WHAT'S WRONG? GO ON AND DRINK.

IT MIGHT HELP YOU FEEL A LITTLE...

RIGHT. WE SHOULDN'T WEAR OUT OUR WELCOME.

LET'S GO, CHISE.

O-OKAY.

THANKS...

WE'LL LET THE PROFES-SORS KNOW, OKAY?

YOU RELAX AND GET SOME REST.

NO ONE'S EVER... SAID THAT TO ME BEFORE.

I'M FREE...?

MISTAKES ARE OKAY...?

BAP

I DON'T UNDERSTAND HOW THIS GREAT SOFTIE THINKS, EITHER.

I HEAR YOU.

I BROUGHT THE WATER.

THANKS, LUCY.

カ!! GA-CHAK
チャ

GRIP
キコ

YOU MEAN "LOOKING OUT FOR YOURSELF"?

WASN'T I JUST EXPLAINING PROPER, UM...SELFISHNESS?

R-RIGHT.

Oops! I got it wrong.

UNTIL RECENTLY, I DIDN'T HAVE ANYONE LIKE THAT MYSELF.

I'M NOT EXACTLY EXPERIENCED AT THIS STUFF, SO I DON'T REALLY KNOW WHAT I'M DOING.

IF YOU EVER WANT TO **TALK**, I'M HERE.

I JUST GOT THE FEELING YOU WERE **HURTING** REALLY BADLY.

THIS IS ALL STUFF OTHER PEOPLE HAVE TOLD ME, BUT--

BUT I GUESS I'M JUST TRYING TO SAY YOU'RE FREE TO DO WHAT *YOU* WANT.

IF SOMETHING DOESN'T WORK, JUST THINK IT OVER AND TRY AGAIN.

YOU DON'T MAKE...

ANY SENSE TO ME.

BUT THE FIRST TIME WE MET, WHEN YOU'D COLLAPSED...

AND I MEAN...

I KNOW THAT'S NOT ENOUGH REASON TO JUST COMPLETELY TRUST SOMEONE.

BUT...

YOU WERE POLITE AND CONSIDERATE WHEN WE TALKED.

YOU THANKED ME AFTERWARDS.

IF YOU WANT TO BE LEFT ALONE, YOU'RE ALLOWED TO SAY SO.

IF DO YOU WANT TO SAY SOMETHING, THAT'S OKAY, TOO.

IF THERE'S SOMETHING YOU DON'T WANT TO SAY, YOU DON'T HAVE TO SAY IT.

I...
I SPIED
ON YOU
AND
ZOE...

I DIDN'T
SPEAK
WHEN YOU
ASKED
ME TO.

I'VE...

NEVER
DONE
ANYTHING
FOR YOU.

SURE,
I GUESS.

SHOULDN'T
YOU
FIND ME
CREEPY...

AND
SUSPI-
CIOUS
...?

CLENCH

UM...

ALCYONE...?

"IS THAT SO," HUH?

Yes?

IS PHILOMELA, ER...

DO YOU THINK YOU CAN DRINK?

OH! UM...

LUCY WENT TO GET WATER FOR YOU.

PHILO-MELA!

DO YOU KEEP LOOKING AFTER ME?

WHY...

Oh.

WE HAD TO BREAK A CONSTRUCT.

WE WERE LEARNING SELF-DEFENSE... IN CASE WE'RE ATTACKED.

OH, UH...

Breaking things invariably causes her great pain.

That would be very hard on her.

Is that so?

THE FIRST TIME I MET HER, SHE'D COLLAPSED.

Even setting that aside, she's been this way for several years.

Doing so leaves her very unwell.

YEARS ...?

I'LL GET HER SOME WATER.

HOW DO YOU FEEL?

WOULD YOU? THANKS.

BTAM

If I search.

IT'LL BE QUICKER IF I GO.

Allow me.

DO YOU KNOW WHERE TO GET IT?

What was today's lesson?

THERE'S NOTHING IN HERE BUT STUDY MATERIALS.

EVEN LUCY HAD A COUPLE OF THROW PILLOWS.

Miss Philomela?

KREEK

SHF...

HERE WE GO.

PHILOMELA STARTED FEELING AWFULLY UNWELL.

YOU'RE... ALCYONE, RIGHT?

SHE'S LIKE... PHILOMELA'S FAMILIAR...? ISH?

WHAT'S WITH THE VAGUE ANSWER?

AND THIS IS...?

FWMP

NNNH...

WE HAVE TO GROW AND MAKE ANYTHING WE NEED.

WITH THE COLLEGE IN LOCKDOWN, *NOTHING* COMES IN.

NOT LIKE WE HAVE MUCH CHOICE NOW.

WELL, YEAH, THE PROF JUST EXPLAINED THAT PART. BUT STILL...

Fruits and veg and all

This super fertilizer sure helps.

HARDLY MEANS YOU KNOW EVERYTHING ABOUT THEM.

KNOWING SOMEONE SINCE THEY WERE LITTLE...

THING IS...

IS THIS IT?

ARE YOU GUYS CHILDHOOD FRIENDS...?

WHEN YOU WERE KIDS?

UM!

WHAT'S WITH EVERYONE TODAY?

NOT LIKE YOU TO COPY SOMEONE ELSE.

HEY, OVER THERE! MOVE *HANDS*, NOT LIPS!

BLORB

BLORB

WE HUNG OUT TOGETHER A LOT AS KIDS.

LOTS OF HOUSES'RE CONNECTED SOMEHOW.

WHY'RE WE *GARDENING* RIGHT AFTER A BUNCH OF CONSTRUCTS TRIED TO THRASH US?

WE ARE!

THAT'S THE LEAST MY HOUSE EXPECTS.

Our village is deep in the mountains.

You actually saw one?

I DIDN'T WANT TO BE OUTDONE.

Whew...! Hot.

YOU COULD BARELY CLIMB TREES.

YOU WEREN'T NEARLY THAT GOOD BACK WHEN WE WERE LITTLE.

・・・・・・

OH? BY WHO?

I'M NOT NAMING NAMES.

YOU WERE AMAZING BACK THERE, RÍAN!

I SAW YOU **SPARRING** WITH THAT PROFESSOR!

I ONLY CAUGHT A BIT, THOUGH.

AMAZING HOW?

CHISE WAS TOO, BUT STILL.

I SAW ONE ONCE WHEN I WAS LITTLE, BUT THAT WAS IT!

YOU WERE LIKE SOME WILDCAT OR MOUNTAIN LION!

WOLVES RUN REALLY FAST, BUT NONE OF THEM CAN JUMP THAT HIGH.

IT JUMPED SO FAR UP THIS HIGH CLIFF!

Chapter 37: Nothing ventured, nothing gained. II

HULLO, HULLO!

WERE YOU WAITING LONG?

Hardly any makeup, I see.

I'M ON MY THIRD GLASS, THANKS.

...It's just you. Why bother?

I TOLD YOU IT WAS A GOOD PROSPECT.

IF IT'S THAT GOOD AND YOU'RE SHARING THE WEALTH, IT *MUST* BE DANGEROUS.

JUST GETTING STARTED, HM?

WELL? WHAT'S THIS DEADLY REQUEST OF YOURS? LET'S HAVE IT.

OH. RIGHT.

IF I'M AWAY FROM YOU TOO LONG, I'LL COLLAPSE.

YOU'RE COMING, TOO?

Look at this

DON'T TALK NONSENSE. LOOK HOW PALE YOU ARE.

JUST...

NO...

NOT... THE NURSE...

AT ANY RATE, CHISE, ARE YOU--?

MY ROOM...

PLEASE...

SURE THING.

Feel better.

Huh?!

I'LL TAKE HER TO THE INFIRMARY.

COULD YOU LET THE NEXT TEACHER KNOW THAT'S WHERE WE ARE?

YOU'LL BE CAREFUL WITH HER, WON'T YOU?

PHILOMELA HAS ALWAYS HAD DELICATE HEALTH.

VERONICA KNOWS PHILOMELA PRETTY WELL.

WOULD SHE KNOW WHY PHILOMELA'S FAMILY WANTS TO PULL HER OUT?

SURE.

PHILOMELA?!

WHAT'S WRONG?

RIGHT--SHE'D COLLAPSED WHEN WE FIRST MET...

YOU CERTAINLY DON'T LOOK FINE.

PHILOMELA LOOKS REALLY ILL!

LET'S GET YOU TO THE INFIRMARY, SHALL WE?

N-NO, I'M FINE.

IT'S NEARLY TIME FOR YOUR NEXT LESSON, STUDENTS.

YANK

OW!

THERE ARE EVEN SOME WHERE THE BOOK *ITSELF* MAY HARBOR SOMETHING--

SOME BELONG TO ALCHEMISTS WHO WENT COMPLETELY OFF THE DEEP END.

SOME ALCHEMISTS USE **CURSE TRAPS** SO NO ONE ELSE CAN EVER READ THEIR BOOK.

ZA--ER, PROFESSOR ZACCHERONI?

C'MON, I SAID THAT HURTS! HOW ARE YOU SO RIDICULOUSLY STRONG?!

MAKE SURE YOU ALL REST AND GET HYDRATED.

Bye now!

GOOD QUESTION. WHY DO YOU THINK?

AND YOU CAN STOP GLARING DAGGERS ANY TIME NOW, OKAY?

WHY DID YOU COME UP FROM BELOW?

ER, PROFESSOR ZACCHE-RONI?

WAS THE BOOK YOU SUMMONED YOUR CONSTRUCTS FROM YOUR SPELL BOOK...?

ALL ALCHEMISTS BUILD UP THEIR OWN SPELL BOOKS.

BEST TO HAVE SOME SPELLS PREPPED AND READY TO GO.

PEOPLE PUT ALL SORTS OF THINGS IN THESE.

YEP, PRETTY MUCH.

YOU KIDS WILL EACH HAVE YOUR OWN ONE DAY.

THE COLLEGE LIBRARY HAS LOTS OF THOSE IN ITS COLLECTION.

SOME ARE KEPT FOR POSTERITY, OTHERS SO THEY CAN BE STUDIED.

THEY CAN BE SPELLS YOU USE REGULARLY, OR THAT ARE FIDDLY TO SET UP.

SOMETIMES WHEN AN ALCHEMIST DIES, THEIR SPELL BOOK GETS COPIED AND PUBLISHED AS REFERENCE MATERIAL.

THE REALLY FAMOUS ONES ARE PRACTICALLY HOUSEHOLD NAMES.

AND, OF COURSE, SOME ARE SAID TO BE TOO DANGEROUS TO OPEN, LET ALONE READ.

IS WHAT'S INSIDE SO BAD?

Meeeee!

NO LYING, YOU TWO.

SO WHO WAS SCARED?

ER...NO, THANKS. ANYWAY! YOU ALL DID GREAT FOR YOUR FIRST TIME.

BUT IF YOU'RE THAT EAGER, I'LL GLADLY PUT SOME MORE HOLES IN YOUR HIDE LATER.

DID I OR DID I NOT TELL YOU TO KEEP THINGS APPROPRIATE FOR A CLASS?

ALCHEMY'S CONVENIENT SOMETIMES, BUT NOT IN ALL SITUATIONS.

SURE, YOU CAN CAST A SPELL ON YOURSELF IN ADVANCE TO DEFLECT BULLETS.

NOT SO MUCH TIME FOR WHIPPING UP ALCHEMY, RIGHT?

SEEMS LIKE A BUNCH OF YOU GOT BANGED UP, HMM?

BUT CAN YOU REALLY MAINTAIN ALL THAT EVERY SINGLE DAY OF YOUR LIFE?

IF YOU ASSESS YOUR SKILL HONESTLY, DO YOU HAVE WHAT IT TAKES FOR THAT?

OR TURN THEIR SPELLS BACK ON THEM.

YES, SOME SPELLS LET YOU DODGE SHRAPNEL AND AVOID BLADES, CURSE YOUR ENEMIES...

THAT'S QUITE ENOUGH OF THAT.

ZACCHERONI. CHILDREN.

AWW. CUTTING US OFF LIKE THAT IS CRUEL, WACHMANN.

EVERYONE HAS PASSED THIS TEST.

WELL DONE.

THUMP

WHEW!

Aaiiee—

DONE!

WSH

GA-KLAK!

THAK!

WH-WHP

BWUK

WHAT'S THAT SOUND ...?

JASMINE, YOUR NOSE IS BLEEDING.

OOF. THAT WAS ROUGHER THAN I THOUGHT.

Wasn't paying attention...

IS EVERYONE ELSE FINISHED, TOO?

TWCH

TWCH

TWCH...

!!!!!

GRIP...

ARE YOU OKAY...?

HM?

OH, AYE. FINE, THANKS.

I WAS A TOTAL DISASTER.

WOW, LOOK AT YOU. NOT A SPOT ON YOU!

I THINK IT'S INCREDIBLE.

DID SOMEBODY TELL YOU THAT WASN'T GOOD ENOUGH?

IF I CAN'T DO AT LEAST THIS MUCH, THEN--

W-WELL...

FSS

WHUD!!!

Ulp!

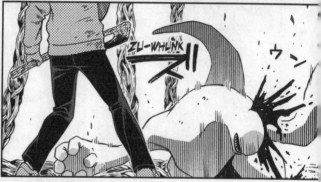

GWOM-!!

NGK!

HRF!

THUD

OOF...! FEELS LIKE THAT WOULD'VE CRUSHED MY RIBS WITHOUT THE AMULET.

HULP!

TOTTER...

I'M NOT SUPPOSED TO USE THESE...!

DWAM

HI+

TALK ABOUT A DANGEROUS ASSIGN-MENT...! BET RIAN'S ALREADY WRAPPED IT UP, THOUGH.

WSH

KISH

KISH

KISH...

KRIK

SWRF...

PA-KRISH

IT
BROKE.

SO,
WANT
TO COME
PLAY
WITH
*ME* FOR
A BIT?

LOOK
AT THAT!
YOU TWO
FINISHED
FAST.

NO
SURPRISE,
SINCE YOU
BOTH HAVE
EXPERI-
ENCE.

PEEK

I'VE NEVER LEARNED ANY OF THAT.

HOW WAS I ABLE TO JUST... DO IT?

RIGHT, I NEED A WEAPON!

EXCEPT... I'VE NEVER USED **ANY** KIND OF WEAPON BEFORE!

AN INVISIBLE WALL...? WE'VE ALL BEEN SPLIT UP.

CLOMP

WELL...NOT SO MUCH A "WALL" AS SPACE YOU CAN'T TOUCH.

AN AL-CHEMICAL SPELL, I GUESS.

CAN YOU DO ANY OF THAT WHILE I'VE GOT YOU LIKE THIS?

ARE YOU STARTING TO SEE WHY ALCHEMISTS' BODYGUARDS ALL LEARN MARKSMANSHIP AND MARTIAL ARTS?

MARTIN!

WHUMP

IT'S AS TRUE FOR ALCHEMISTS AS FOR NORMAL PEOPLE.

BASHING, STABBING, OR SHOOTING ARE ALL FASTER, EASIER WAYS TO KILL.

IT TAKES *WAY* TOO LONG! ONLY AN ASTOUNDING ALCHEMIST CAN MOVE FAST ENOUGH.

SPELLS TAKE FOCUS. CONTROL. PREPARA-TION.

SO! READY OR NOT, WE'RE GETTING STARTED!

...ZU

ZU ZU∞...°

HMM?

UM...

AREN'T WE GOING TO USE ALCHEMY TO FIGHT BACK...?

GOTTA GET A FEEL FOR A REAL ONE FIRST.

AVOID GUNS, THOUGH, OKAY? THEY'RE NOT BAD, BUT THERE'S A TRICK TO 'EM.

AHA HA HA HA!

YOU'RE HILARI-OUS, KID!

DO WE REALLY HAVE TO USE WEAPONS?

THERE ARE SPELLS FOR REPELLING PROJECTILES OR TURNING SPELLS BACK ON THEIR CASTER. THOSE SEEM USEFUL.

GWAP

RUFA
RUFA RUFA
RUFA

BAFF

HA
HA
HA!

GETTING ATTACKED OUTTA THE BLUE IS SCARY, HUH?!

TAP

GOOD, YOUR AMULET'S WORKING.

AND THAT'S WHY CLASSES LIKE THIS GO ON THE ROSTER.

AT LEAST SOMEONE'S HAVING FUN.

KNIVES, QUARTER-STAVES, WHATEVER. ANYTHING GOES.

VIVIDLY.

VISUALIZE IT...

W-WEAP-ONS...?

Webster, someone can stand in for you.

Yes, sir...

Want me to?

EVERYONE GRAB A CLAY BLOCK AND VISUALIZE A WEAPON OR ITEM YOU THINK YOU'LL BE ABLE TO USE.

JUST A LITTLE INFUSION OF MAGIC, RIGHT?

FUWA...

IF YOU DON'T, THEY'RE JUST ROCKS ON STRINGS.

I ASSUME YOU KNOW HOW TO ACTIVATE THEM?

BUT PEOPLE COMING AFTER ALCHEMISTS USUALLY WANT ONE THING.

IF THE GOAL WAS TO GIVE US A BEATING, WE'D BE LUCKY.

THERE'RE ENEMIES ABOUT.

THE COLLEGE IS IN LOCKDOWN, WHICH MEANS...

OUR LIVES.

"REQUIRED
CLASSES"
...?

CLAY
BLOCKS...
WITH
INSET
STONES?

THE
AMULETS
OFFER
SOME
PROTEC-
TION
AGAINST
WOUNDS.

FIRST,
YOU'LL
NEED
ONE OF
THESE.

JANGLE

PUT 'EM ON
SECURELY.
YOU DO
*NOT* WANT
TO LOSE
THEM.

RUNED
AMULETS?

AND...

Chapter 71: Nothing ventured, nothing gained. I

WHERE DO YOU WANT?

Where are you right now?

HULLO? THIS IS IZAK.

Chester. Why? I'm moving again tomorrow.

Do for what?

YOU'LL DO, THEN.

It's Marielle.

THERE'S GOOD MONEY TO BE MADE. COME TO LONDON.